SALTWATER JOYS

WRITTEN BY WAYNE CHAULK

ILLUSTRATED BY DAWN BAKER

SALTWATER JOYS

WRITTEN BY WAYNE CHAULK

ILLUSTRATED BY DAWN BAKER

Pennywell Books
St. John's, NL

Library and Archives Canada Cataloguing in Publication

Chaulk, Wayne
    Saltwater joys / written by Wayne Chaulk ; illustrated by Dawn Baker.

 Also issued in electronic format.
ISBN 978-1-77117-213-4 (bound).-- ISBN 978-1-77117-028-4 (pbk.).

    1. Newfoundland and Labrador--Juvenile poetry.
I. Baker, Dawn, 1962- II. Title.

PS8605.H395S35 2012   jC811'.6   C2012-904542-X

PRINTED IN CANADA

This paper has been certified to meet the environmental and social standards of the Forest Stewardship Council® (FSC®) and comes from responsibly managed forests, and verified recycled sources.

Pennywell Books is an imprint of Flanker Press Limited.

FLANKER PRESS LTD.
PO BOX 2522, STATION C
ST. JOHN'S, NL A1C 6K1 CANADA

TELEPHONE: (709) 739-4477   TOLL-FREE: 1-866-739-4420   FAX: (709) 739-4420

WWW.FLANKERPRESS.COM

4 5 6 7 8 9 10

Cover Design and Book Layout: Peter Hanes

"Saltwater Joys" lead sheet by Eric West
"Saltwater Joys" can be found in:
Eric West, *All Together Now: Songs of Newfoundland and Labrador, Volume 3* (Ladle Cove, NL: Vinland Music, 2000)
Eric West, *Buddy Wasisname and the Other Fellers – Songbook 3: The First 20 Years* (Ladle Cove, NL: Vinland Music, 2005)
Eric West, *Newfoundland Explorations: 15 Easy Pieces for Guitar* (Ladle Cove, NL: Vinland Music, 2011)

    Canada Council for the Arts   Conseil des Arts du Canada

We acknowledge the financial support of the Government of Canada through the Canada Book Fund (CBF) and the Government of Newfoundland and Labrador, Department of Business, Tourism, Culture and Rural Development for our publishing activities. We acknowledge the support of the Canada Council for the Arts, which last year invested $153 million to bring the arts to Canadians throughout the country. *Nous remercions le Conseil des arts du Canada de son soutien. L'an dernier, le Conseil a investi 153 millions de dollars pour mettre de l'art dans la vie des Canadiennes et des Canadiens de tout le pays.*

Most of "Saltwater Joys" was written while sitting on a rock on the Beal O' Da Point just out from Clayton's wharf here in Charlottetown. The wharf is on the beach just down from the house where I spent my childhood.

I believe it was the thousands of hours spent playing, fishing, dabbling, rafting, rowing, swimming, looking, listening and smelling that gave me the credentials to write the song. I will always treasure the time spent in this little piece of paradise where "Saltwater Joys" was created.

This book came about because Dawn borrowed a multitude of my photos and proceeded to paint for three straight months. The resulting seventeen paintings, which so nicely grace these pages, depict many of the sites that inspired the lyrics of the song.

So it's our hope that you will thumb through the pages, ponder the images and, if you like, just break into song!

Wayne

Just to wake up in the morning to the quiet of the cove.

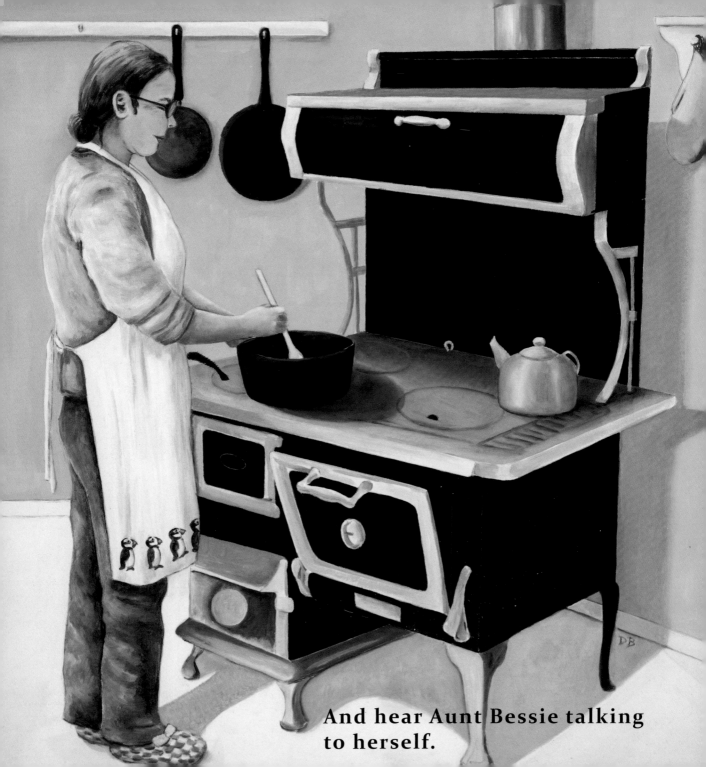

And hear Aunt Bessie talking to herself.

And to hear poor Uncle John mumbling wishes to old Nell. It made me feel like everything was fine.

I was born down by the water and
it's here I'm goin' to stay.

I've searched for all the reasons
why I should go away.

But I haven't got the thirst for all those modern-day toys, so I'll just take my chances with those saltwater joys.

Following the little brook as it trickles
to the shore, in the autumn when the
trees are flaming red.

Kicking leaves that fall around me.

Watching sunsets paint the hills.
That's all I'll ever need to feel at home.

This island that we cling to has been handed down with pride.

By folks that fought to live here, taking hardships all in stride.

So I'll compliment her beauty, hold on to my goodbyes,
and I'll stay and take my chances with those saltwater joys.

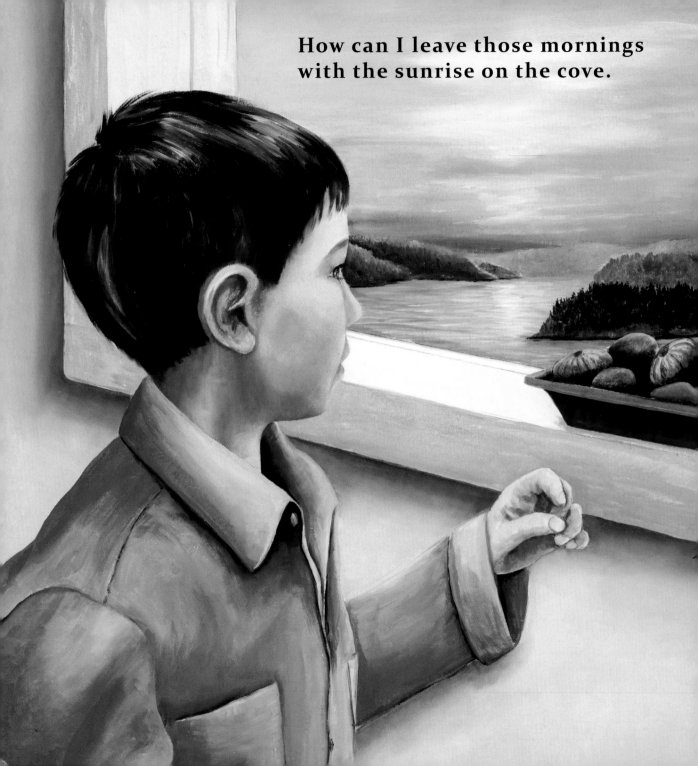

How can I leave those mornings
with the sunrise on the cove.

And the gulls like flies surrounding Clayton's wharf.

Platter's Island wrapped in rainbow
in the evening after fog.

The ocean smells are perfume to my soul.

ome go to where the buildings reach to meet the clouds,
here warm and gentle people turn to swarmin', faceless
owds. So I'll do without their riches, glamour and the noise.

And I'll stay and take my chances with those saltwater joys.

Saltwater Joys

Wayne Chaulk

1. Just to wake up in the morn - ing to the qui - et of the cove And

hear Aunt Bes - sie talk - ing to her - self And to

hear poor Un - cle John mumb - ling wish - es to old Nell It

made me feel like ev - ery - thing was fine. I was

born down by the wa - ter and it's here I'm goin' to stay I've

searched for all the rea - sons why I should go a - way But I

have - n't got the thirst for all those mod - ern - day toys So

I'll just take my chanc - es with those salt - wat - er joys.

Following the little brook as it trickles to the shore
In the autumn when the trees are flaming red
Kicking leaves that fall around me
Watching sunsets paint the hills
That's all I'll ever need to feel at home.

This island that we cling to has been handed down with pride
By folks that fought to live here, taking hardships all in stride
So I'll compliment her beauty, hold on to my goodbyes
And I'll stay and take my chances with those saltwater joys.

How can I leave those mornings with the sunrise on the cove
And the gulls like flies surrounding Clayton's wharf
Platter's Island wrapped in rainbow in the evening after fog
The ocean smells are perfume to my soul.

Some go to where the buildings reach to meet the clouds
Where warm and gentle people turn to swarmin', faceless crowds
So I'll do without their riches, glamour and the noise
And I'll stay and take my chances with those saltwater joys.

Wayne Chaulk was born in Charlottetown, Newfoundland. After graduating from Memorial University, Wayne returned to his beloved Bonavista Bay, and for the next fifteen years, he devoted himself to his teaching career. But when Ray Johnson and Kevin Blackmore moved to Glovertown, the die was cast, and Buddy Wasisname and the Other Fellers was born. Wayne turned his affection for rural Newfoundland and its people to the craft of songwriting, and the result has been a collection of lyrical gems, such as "Saltwater Joys."

Dawn Baker has been a full-time visual artist and children's writer since 1992. She grew up in Glenwood, Newfoundland, and has lived in Gander since she was a teenager. Dawn has a bachelor of education (post-secondary) and a certificate in library studies, both from Memorial University, and has served on the board of directors of The Rooms Corporation of Newfoundland and Labrador since 2006.